nickelodeon

降去神通

AVATAR

THE LAST AIRBENDER

SMOKE AND SHADOW · PART ONE

script
GENE LUEN YANG

art and cover
GURIHIRU

lettering
MICHAEL HEISLER

DARK HORSE BOOKS

president and publisher
MIKE RICHARDSON

editor
DAVE MARSHALL

associate editor
AARON WALKER

collection designer
JUSTIN COUCH

digital art technician
CHRISTINA McKENZIE

Special thanks to Linda Lee, Kat van Dam, James Salerno, and Joan Hilty
at Nickelodeon, and to Bryan Konietzko and Michael Dante DiMartino.

Published by **Dark Horse Books**
A division of Dark Horse Comics, Inc.
10956 SE Main Street, Milwaukie, OR 97222

DarkHorse.com
Nick.com

International Licensing: (503) 905-2377
Comic Shop Locator Service: (888) 266-4226

Scholastic edition: July 2016 | ISBN 978-1-50670-281-0

1 3 5 7 9 10 8 6 4 2
Printed in Canada

nickelodeon™

降击神通

AVATAR

THE LAST AIRBENDER™

Created by
Bryan Konietzko
Michael Dante DiMartino

MY SPIES REPORT THAT THE *"FIRE LORD"* WILL RETURN TO OUR SHORES TOMORROW.

HE'LL HAVE WITH HIM A SMALL GROUP OF *COMPANIONS,* INCLUDING HIS MOTHER, THE TRAITOROUS *URSA!*

BOO!

DURING HIS JOURNEY FROM *HARBOR CITY* TO THE *ROYAL PALACE,* ZUKO WILL BE *VULNERABLE* FOR LONG STRETCHES.

SO TOMORROW-- TOMORROW IS *OUR* DAY!

TOMORROW, WE REMOVE ZUKO NOT ONLY FROM THE *THRONE,* BUT FROM THE *FACE OF THE EARTH!*

TOMORROW, WE RESTORE THE FIRE NATION TO GLORY!

TOMORROW, WE ATTACK!

YEAH!

POWER TO THE FIRE NATION!

FREE FIRE LORD OZAI!

HA HA!

WHEEE!

SURE LOOKS LIKE AANG AND KIYI ARE HAVING FUN.

WHY DON'T YOU ASK TO JOIN THEM, SOKKA?

NO THANKS. TOO *SLIMY* FOR MY TASTE.

FLYING DOLPHIN-FISHES AREN'T SLIMY!

YEAH, WELL, I STILL PREFER MY RIDES TO BE *MECHANICAL*.

RAAARRR!

EXCEPT YOU, OF COURSE, APPA!

LICK

IT'LL BE *SO GOOD* TO FINALLY HAVE YOU HOME AGAIN.

I'M GONNA GO SEE WHAT AANG AND THE OTHERS ARE UP TO.

URSA? YOU OKAY?

WHY WOULDN'T I BE?

WHENEVER YOU'RE SCARED, YOUR HANDS GET *COLD*.

WE USED TO HOLD HANDS BEFORE PERFORMANCES, REMEMBER? ON OPENING NIGHTS, IT FELT LIKE HOLDING A *BLOCK OF ICE*.

IT'S JUST BEEN A LONG TIME SINCE I'VE BEEN IN... *THAT PLACE.*

I'LL BE FINE, NOREN.

=GASP!= KIYI!

13

ALL RIGHT, HONEY. WHATEVER YOU WANT.

...

GIVE HER TIME.

I KNOW. NOT EVERY LITTLE GIRL HAS TO DEAL WITH HER MOTHER *CHANGING FACES*.

URSA, I'M *SO SORRY* I WORRIED YOU! BUT BELIEVE ME, FLYING DOLPHIN-FISHES ARE AMONG THE GENTLEST CREATURES IN THE WORLD!

NO, AVATAR. I'M THE ONE WHO SHOULD BE SORRY. I'M *EMBARRASSED* THAT I OVERREACTED LIKE THAT.

NOW, IF YOU'LL EXCUSE ME...

ding! ding!

TY LEE! IT'S BEEN SO LONG!

MICHI! TOM-TOM! I DIDN'T KNOW YOU GUYS WOULD BE HERE! DOES THAT MEAN MASTER UKANO IS HERE TOO?

NO. NO, HE'S *NOT*.

THE END OF THE WAR WAS HARD ON HIM -- ON ALL OF US, REALLY -- BUT HE *CROSSED THE LINE.* I FINALLY REALIZED THAT HE CARES MORE ABOUT *POLITICS* THAN HIS OWN CHILDREN'S *SAFETY.*

SO WE'RE HERE NOW, ON OUR OWN.

OH. I'M SORRY.

DON'T BE. LIVING WITH MURA HAS BEEN WONDERFUL!

OH, THE PLEASURE'S ALL MINE! NICE HAVING SOME COMPANY FOR A CHANGE!

FLOWERS AREN'T FOR EATING, TOM-TOM.

THEN HOW COME THEY'RE SO *YUMMY?*

16

YOU EXPECTING SOMEONE, TY LEE? YOU KEEP LOOKING AROUND.

NO, I... IT'S *STUPID*. YOU KNOW ZUKO LEFT TOWN, RIGHT?

TO SEARCH FOR HIS MOM, I'D HEARD.

WELL, HE TOOK *AZULA* WITH HIM.

HE LET THAT *LUNATIC* OUT OF PRISON?! SO HE REALLY *IS* TURNING INTO HIS FATHER.

I DON'T THINK IT WAS *THAT*.

EVEN SO, I'VE HAD A HARD TIME MAINTAINING A *PEACEFUL AURA* EVER SINCE.

A PART OF ME EXPECTS HER TO...I DON'T KNOW...POP OUT OF NOWHERE AT *ANY MOMENT* --

-- TO *PUNISH US* FOR BETRAYING HER.

YEAH. SOMETHING LIKE THAT.

YOU KNOW WHAT? LET'S TALK ABOUT SOMETHING ELSE.

ARE YOU SEEING ANYONE NEW?

EH. I DID MEET THIS GUY NAMED *KEI LO.*

"A COUPLE MONTHS AGO, HE CAME INTO THE SHOP, BOUGHT SOME FLOWERS, THEN TURNED AROUND AND GAVE THEM TO ME."

AW, HOW *ROMANTIC!* IS HE CUTE?

I GUESS... FOR A *PATSY.* TURNS OUT HE WAS WORKING FOR MY *DAD.*

MY DAD'S BEEN RUNNING THIS SECRET SOCIETY OF *NUTJOBS* BENT ON OVERTHROWING ZUKO. THEY CALL THEMSELVES THE *NEW OZAI SOCIETY.*

OH, NO!

"HE SENT KEI LO TO RECRUIT ME. I DIDN'T GO FOR IT, OF COURSE.

"WHEN I TOLD MY MOM ABOUT DAD'S LITTLE HOBBY, SHE LEFT HIM. HE WAS ENDANGERING ALL OF US, YOU KNOW? ESPECIALLY *TOM-TOM.*"

THAT'S WHY WE'RE LIVING WITH AUNTIE MURA NOW.

I'M SO SORRY, MAI!

BUT I PROMISE YOU, NOT ALL GUYS ARE *JERKS.*

THERE'S *MORE.* FOR THE PAST COUPLE WEEKS, KEI LO'S BEEN VISITING ME IN *SECRET.*

WAIT, WHAT?! SO YOU GUYS *ARE* DATING?

NO. *PATSIES* AREN'T MY TYPE. BUT I THINK MAYBE I CAN *USE* KEI LO TO STOP MY DAD.

STOP YOUR DAD FROM *HURTING ZUKO.*

HEY, JUST DOING *MY DUTY* AS A LOYAL CITIZEN OF THE FIRE NATION.

ANYWAY, EARLIER TODAY, KEI LO CAME TO TELL ME THAT THE NEW OZAI SOCIETY'S GOT *BIG PLANS* FOR TOMORROW.

ZUKO'S SUPPOSED TO COME BACK TOMORROW!

I KNOW. THAT'S WHY I ASKED YOU HERE. I WANT YOU TO GET A READ ON HIM, TO SEE IF HE'S TELLING THE *TRUTH.*

HERE HE COMES.

OVER HERE, BABE!

"BABE"?

KEI LO, MEET MY FRIEND TY LEE.

HI...

YOU GUYS ARE LEAVING? ALREADY?

YEP.

GOING BACK TO THE CAPITAL CITY IS GOING TO BRING UP ALL SORTS OF STUFF FOR YOUR *MOM*, FOR *KIYI*, FOR *ALL OF YOU*.

YOU NEED TO FIGURE IT OUT AS A *FAMILY*.

WE'D JUST BE IN THE WAY. ESPECIALLY *DOLPHIN-FISH RIDER* OVER HERE.

YOU GUYS HAVEN'T REALLY HAD ANY *BONDING TIME* YET, ZUKO. THIS WILL BE YOUR CHANCE.

I GUESS THAT MAKES SENSE.

THANK YOU, GUYS, FOR EVERYTHING.

HAPPY TO BE THERE FOR YOU, BUDDY!

...SO THAT'S IT. THAT'S THE NEW OZAI SOCIETY'S *BIG PLAN.*

WITH ZUKO GONE AND AZULA MISSING, THE STAGE WILL BE CLEARED FOR *OZAI* TO RETURN TO POWER.

YOU'RE *SO BRAVE* TO BRING THIS INFORMATION TO US, KEI LO! I'M *SO IMPRESSED!*

I DON'T EVEN WANT TO *THINK* ABOUT WHAT THE OTHER SOCIETY MEMBERS WOULD DO TO ME IF THEY FOUND OUT I WAS MEETING WITH A *KYOSHI WARRIOR.*

I DON'T GET IT. WHY TAKE THE RISK?

LET'S JUST SAY, YOU DON'T MEET SOMEONE LIKE *MAI* EVERY DAY.

NO, I GUESS YOU *DON'T.*

I SHOULD GET GOING. THANK YOU, MAI, FOR BELIEVING ME.

OH, WITH THOSE EYES, HOW COULD I NOT?

BYE, BABE!

HE'S OUT OF EARSHOT. YOU CAN STOP BEING SO FAKE NOW!

WELL?

WHAT IS GOING ON WITH YOU?! HOW COULD YOU LEAD HIM ON LIKE THAT?!

WHAT'S THE BIG DEAL? THAT'S EXACTLY WHAT *HE* DID TO *ME* WHEN WE FIRST MET!

BESIDES, WHAT *I'M* DOING IS FOR A *GOOD CAUSE*.

THERE ARE WAYS OF PROTECTING YOUR *EX-BOYFRIEND* THAT DON'T INVOLVE *SELLING YOUR SOUL*.

WHATEVER.

SO WHAT DO YOU THINK? IS HE LYING OR NOT?

THAT BOY'S GOT A *GOOD AURA*. I THINK HE'S BEING *TRUTHFUL*.

WHICH IS MORE THAN I CAN SAY ABOUT *YOU* RIGHT NOW.

DID AANG, KATARA, AND SOKKA JUST LEAVE?

YES. IF I'D KNOWN YOU WERE STILL UP, I WOULD'VE ASKED YOU TO COME SAY GOODBYE.

YOU'RE LUCKY TO HAVE SUCH GOOD FRIENDS.

I AM.

WHAT'S GOING ON, MOM?

JUST NEEDED A LITTLE FRESH AIR, THAT'S ALL.

KIYI WILL COME AROUND SOON. YOU'RE THE SAME PERSON ON THE INSIDE, REGARDLESS OF WHAT YOU LOOK LIKE ON THE OUTSIDE. SHE'LL FIGURE IT OUT.

I KNOW SHE WILL.

29

UGH!

NEPHEW!

UNCLE!

THANK *YOU* FOR WATCHING OVER THINGS WHILE I'VE BEEN AWAY. ONCE AGAIN, I DON'T KNOW HOW TO REPAY YOU.

SEEING THAT YOUR TRIP WAS SUCCESSFUL IS REPAYMENT ENOUGH!

IROH!

LADY URSA, I'M DEEPLY GRATEFUL FOR THE OPPORTUNITY TO SEE YOU AGAIN!

LET ME EXPRESS HOW SORRY I AM FOR ALL THE PAIN YOU SUFFERED AT THE HANDS OF *MY FAMILY.*

IROH, WHAT ARE YOU APOLOGIZING FOR? *YOUR* PRESENCE IN THE FAMILY ALWAYS GAVE ME *HOPE.*

SUKI, THANK YOU FOR TAKING CARE OF ALL THIS.

NO PROBLEM, ZUKO! THE MESSENGER HAWK GOT BACK TO US JUST A FEW HOURS AGO, SO WE REALLY HAD TO *HUSTLE.*

BUT WE'RE PREPARED TO FOLLOW *YOUR PLAN* DOWN TO THE LAST DETAIL!

I'LL ESCORT YOU AND YOUR FAMILY TO THE PALACE ALONG A *HIDDEN ROUTE* WHILE A *DECOY* TRAVELS UP THE MAIN ROAD.

SO YOU WERE ABLE TO FIND A DECOY, THEN? WHO?

WELL... IROH SORT OF VOLUNTEERED.

NO OFFENSE, UNCLE, BUT YOU AND I DON'T REALLY LOOK ALIKE.

OH, THE CROWDS WON'T SEE MY *FACE*, JUST MY *HAND*.

WHAT DO YOU THINK? IS MY HAND-WAVING FILLED WITH ENOUGH *ANGST*?

I'VE BEEN PRACTICING ALL MORNING.

WE SHOULD GET GOING!

SURE.

SHE'S PRETTY! DON'T YOU THINK, ZUKO?

KIYI, THE PLANK IS PRETTY NARROW. WHY DON'T YOU TAKE YOUR MOTHER'S HAND?

I'M OLD ENOUGH TO WALK ON MY OWN!

I KNOW, BUT MAYBE *SHE'S* SCARED. SHE'S NEVER BEEN ON A SUBMARINE BEFORE.

THAT'S HER PROBLEM!

WILL YOU DO IT AS A FAVOR TO ME?

FINE.

LET'S GET MOVING.

I *LOVE* BEING A KYOSHI WARRIOR, I REALLY DO, BUT THIS GETUP -- *UGH!* I FEEL LIKE I'M SUFFOCATING IN HERE!

A WATCHTOWER EVERY HUNDRED YARDS OR SO...A NARROW ROAD THAT FORCES YOU TO TRAVEL SINGLE FILE...

FIRE LORD SOZIN KNEW WHAT HE WAS DOING WHEN HE DESIGNED THESE SWITCHBACKS.

WHAT ARE YOU TALKING ABOUT, MAI?

THIS IS PROBABLY THE *MOST HEAVILY FORTIFIED ROAD* IN ALL THE FIRE NATION. WHY WOULD MY DAD CHOOSE TO ATTACK HERE, IN BROAD DAYLIGHT?

HE'S A LOT OF THINGS, BUT *STUPID* ISN'T ONE OF THEM.

KEI LO'S A *LIAR.*

38

40

IROH! YOU OKAY IN THERE?

OH, YES! THE DRAGON OF THE WEST IS READY FOR--

--ACTION?

GOOD WORK, EVERYONE! AND SO QUICK!

TOO QUICK. MY DAD'S GATHERED AN *ARMY,* YET HE SENDS *THESE* FIVE BUFFOONS TO TAKE OUT ZUKO?

DOESN'T ADD UP.

WHAT'S YOUR GAME, NUTJOB?

NGH! YOU WON'T GET ANYTHING OUTTA ME!

POWER TO THE FIRE NATION! FREE FIRE LORD OZAI!

FREE FIRE LORD OZAI!

POWER TO THE FIRE NATION!

FREE FIRE LORD OZAI! POWER TO THE FIRE NATION!

READY YOURSELVES, SISTERS! WE'RE IN FOR A *FIGHT!*

STAY PUT.

DON'T BE *SCARED*, KIYI. YOUR BROTHER'S THE MOST POWERFUL MAN IN THE NATION.

WHO SAID ANYTHING ABOUT BEING *SCARED?*

ACK! YOUR HANDS ARE SO COLD!

DON'T TOUCH ME!

IMPOSTOR! IMPOSTOR! IMPOSTOR!

45

IMPOSTOR! IMPOSTOR!

ZUKO! THE TIME HAS COME FOR YOU TO RETURN THE THRONE TO THE *ONE TRUE FIRE LORD!*

WE *DEMAND* THAT YOU STEP DOWN *AT ONCE!*

DO SO *PEACEFULLY* AND *NO HARM* SHALL COME TO YOUR FAMILY!

LET ME GET THIS STRAIGHT.

YOU EXPECT ME TO GIVE UP MY *DESTINY* -- MY *RIGHTFUL PLACE* IN THE NATION -- JUST BECAUSE A BUNCH OF *THUGS* TOO COWARDLY TO SHOW THEIR FACES ASKED ME TO?

RIDICULOUS.

WELL... *YES.*

FWOOOM!!

47

HA HA. NOT BAD FOR A...

WHAT WAS THAT YOU CALLED US AGAIN?

OH YES. *"A BUNCH OF THUGS."*

REMEMBER WHAT I SAID? *NO HARM* WOULD COME TO YOUR FAMILY IF YOU STEPPED DOWN *PEACEFULLY.*

WHAT JUST HAPPENED HERE WAS *NOT PEACEFUL.*

NOT IN THE *LEAST.*

FWOOM!

FWOOM!

LEAVE THEM ALONE! THEY'VE GOT NOTHING TO DO WITH THIS!

THIS IS WRONG...

MASTER, I WON'T LET YOU HURT THOSE PEOPLE!

HURRY, GO SAVE YOUR FAMILY!

WHAT--?

50

YOU! I KNEW YOU COULDN'T BE TRUSTED!

MAI, THE SOCIETY *KNEW* I WAS GOING TO BETRAY THEM! THEY FED ME *BAD INFORMATION*, I SWEAR!

I VOUCH FOR HIM.

WHAT?! YOU DON'T KNOW A THING ABOUT HIM!

I KNOW HIS NAME IS *KEI LO* AND HE JUST HELPED ME SAVE MY *FAMILY!*

BWOF!

NEW OZAI SOCIETY, THE CARRIAGE IS UNGUARDED!

ATTACK! ATTACK WITHOUT MERCY!

I'D KNOW THAT VOICE ANYWHERE.

HAVE YOU LOST YOUR *MIND?!* THIS IS *TREASON!*

YOU'VE NEVER BEEN ABLE TO SEE PAST YOUR OWN *NEEDS*, MY DAUGHTER!

!

STOP! STOP!

I MEANT *ZUKO*, NOT *HER!*

BUT YOU SAID TO ATTACK WITHOUT MERCY!

YOU GOTTA EASE UP ON HER, BUDDY. BOSS'S ORDERS.

TELL *HER* THAT!

WHUMP!

!

ATTACK *HIM*, YOU IMBECILES! NO *MERCY* FOR KEI LO!

SO WHO GETS MERCY? I'M SO *CONFUSED.*

WHUMP!

AAAH!

WACK!

LOOK, MAI, I KNOW YOU DON'T *TRUST* ME RIGHT NOW --

NEWS FLASH. I *NEVER* TRUSTED YOU, *"BABE."*

MY DAD PLAYED YOU FOR A *PATSY*, AND SO DID I.

MAYBE I DESERVE THAT, BUT I'M TRYING TO SHOW YOU NOW:

I REALLY DO *LIKE* YOU.

IF HE'S SUCH A *WEAKLING,* WHY ARE ALL YOUR NUT-JOB FOLLOWERS EITHER *SURRENDERING* OR *FLEEING* FOR THEIR LIVES?

BUT THAT JUST REINFORCES MY POINT, MAI.

ZUKO HAS NO PROBLEM STRONG-ARMING *HIS OWN PEOPLE,* BUT IT'S THE *REST OF THE WORLD* HE SHOULD BE WORRIED ABOUT.

AND *YOU* -- YOU WERE HIS ONLY *REAL* FIRE NATION FRIEND, YET HE PUSHED YOU *AWAY.*

IF YOU DON'T THINK THERE'S ANY *TRUTH* IN WHAT I'M SAYING, GO AHEAD.

ARREST ME.

OW.

OW OW.

OW.

YOU PLANNING TO HOBBLE ALL THE WAY BACK TO THE CAPITAL CITY?

IT'S, WHAT, FIVE MILES AWAY? *TEN*, TOPS? I CAN MAKE IT.

NO, YOU CAN'T. COME ON. WE'LL CATCH A RIDE ON THE KYOSHI WARRIORS' AIRSHIP.

WHERE'S YOUR DAD?

...

HE *GOT AWAY.*

MAI, I'M TELLING YOU, HE HAD MY NUMBER THE *WHOLE TIME.* HE KNEW I WAS SECRETLY MEETING WITH YOU.

I KNOW.

I BELIEVE YOU, KEI LO.

HERE WE ARE.

WOW! I KNEW IT'D BE *BIG*, BUT I DIDN'T THINK IT'D BE *THIS BIG!* COME ON, DADDY! LET'S GO *EXPLORING!*

KIYI, MAYBE WE SHOULD REST FIRST? WE'VE HAD A PRETTY...*DRAMATIC* AFTERNOON.

AW, WHAT'S THE *BIG DEAL?* I KNEW ZUZU WOULD KEEP US SAFE THE WHOLE TIME!

COME ON, COME ON!

"ZUZU"? WHERE'D SHE PICK THAT UP?

I'M NOT SURE.

GOTTA ADMIT, IT SOUNDS MUCH *NICER* COMING FROM *HER* THAN *AZULA.*

STEP

MOM...?

JUST TIRED FROM ALL THE EXCITEMENT.

I'LL HAVE SOMEONE SHOW YOU TO YOUR OLD ROOM.

ONE OF THE GUEST ROOMS WILL BE FINE.

UNCLE!

AGAIN, THANK YOU FOR YOUR HELP.

MY PLEASURE! THESE OLD LEGS NEEDED A STRETCH.

YOU THINK SHE'LL BE OKAY?

TIME HEALS ALL WOUNDS.

THERE'S SOMETHING ELSE BOTHERING YOU, NEPHEW. IT'S NOT JUST YOUR FAMILY.

IT'S THE *NEW OZAI SOCIETY.*

I'VE HAD TO DEAL WITH *OPPOSITION* OF ONE KIND OR ANOTHER SINCE I BECAME FIRE LORD, BUT THIS ONE FELT DIFFERENT. MORE *SERIOUS.* I HAVE ANOTHER FAVOR TO ASK, UNCLE IROH.

WOULD YOU BE WILLING TO ATTEND THE *YU DAO INAUGURATION CEREMONY* IN MY STEAD? THERE'S SO MUCH GOING ON...I THINK I NEED TO *STAY.*

I WAS ABOUT TO SUGGEST THE SAME THING! YOU'RE GROWING IN WISDOM, ZUKO.

BECAUSE I'M BEGINNING TO THINK LIKE YOU?

WELL... *YES.*

ONE MONTH LATER.

CAN'T BELIEVE YOU WOULDN'T GO OUT WITH ME UNTIL MY LEG HEALED.

CASTS ARE SO *UNATTRACTIVE*.

THAT WASN'T IT. IT TOOK YOU THIS LONG TO *TRUST* ME. I MEAN, *REALLY* TRUST ME.

MAYBE, BUT THAT'S BECAUSE YOU DON'T MAKE *SENSE* TO ME. I STILL DON'T GET WHY YOU WOULD BETRAY THE *NEW OZAI SOCIETY*.

I'VE TOLD YOU OVER AND OVER! IT'S BECAUSE OF *YOU*.

EXACTLY. THAT MAKES *NO SENSE*.

I LOST MY *PARENTS* WHEN I WAS YOUNG. SINCE THEN, I'VE BEEN BOUNCED FROM ONE PLACE TO ANOTHER.

I JOINED THE *SOCIETY* BECAUSE I WANTED TO *BELONG* TO SOMETHING. I COULDN'T CARE LESS ABOUT ALL THAT POLITICAL STUFF.

AND NOW?

MEETING YOU MADE ME REALIZE THAT I DON'T WANT TO BELONG TO SOME*THING* ANYMORE.

I WANT TO BELONG TO SOME*ONE*.

YOU HAVE TO GET *OUR BOY* BACK!

HE MUST BE SO *SCARED!*

SOUNDS LIKE YOU GOT THE CLOSEST LOOK AT THE KIDNAPPERS, MAI. CAN YOU DESCRIBE THEM?

THEY LOOKED LIKE THE *KEMURIKAGE.*

SAY AGAIN?

THE KEMURIKAGE.

MY PARENTS USED TO TELL ME ABOUT THEM WHEN I WAS LITTLE, WHENEVER I DID SOMETHING BAD. THEY'RE FROM AN OLD LEGEND -- SPIRITS WHO LIVE IN THE MOUNTAINS OF OUR HOMETOWN.

SUPPOSEDLY, WHEN CHILDREN MISBEHAVE, THE KEMURIKAGE COME AND SNATCH THEM AWAY IN THE MIDDLE OF THE NIGHT.

OH, MAI! YOUR FATHER AND I TOLD YOU THOSE STORIES TO HELP YOU BUILD *CHARACTER!*

OUR PARENTS DID THE SAME FOR *US!* ALL THE PARENTS IN OUR VILLAGE TOLD THOSE STORIES!

THE *KEMURIKAGE* AREN'T SUPPOSED TO BE *REAL!*

BUT IT SEEMS THAT THEY *ARE.*

THE STORY CONTINUES!

Aang and Zuko uncover the secrets of the Kemurikage in . . .

SMOKE AND SHADOW · PART TWO

Avatar: The Last Airbender—The Promise Library Edition
978-1-61655-074-5 $39.99

Avatar: The Last Airbender—The Promise Part 1
978-1-59582-811-8 $10.99

Avatar: The Last Airbender—The Promise Part 2
978-1-59582-875-0 $10.99

Avatar: The Last Airbender—The Promise Part 3
978-1-59582-941-2 $10.99

Avatar: The Last Airbender—The Search Library Edition
978-1-61655-226-8 $39.99

Avatar: The Last Airbender—The Search Part 1
978-1-61655-054-7 $10.99

Avatar: The Last Airbender—The Search Part 2
978-1-61655-190-2 $10.99

Avatar: The Last Airbender—The Search Part 3
978-1-61655-184-1 $10.99

Avatar: The Last Airbender—The Art of the Animated Series
978-1-59582-504-9 $34.99

Avatar: The Last Airbender—The Lost Adventures
978-1-59582-748-7 $14.99

AVAILABLE AT YOUR LOCAL COMICS SHOP OR BOOKSTORE.
To find a comics shop in your area, call 1-888-266-4226
For more information or to order direct, visit DarkHorse.com or call 1-800-862-0052